Bible
Sticker Activity
The Good
Samaritan
and other stories

Retold by Vic Parker

MiLes
KeLLY

First published in 2012 by Miles Kelly Publishing Ltd
Harding's Barn, Bardfield End Green, Thaxted, Essex, CM6 3PX, UK

This edition printed 2018

4 6 8 10 9 7 5 3

Publishing Director Belinda Gallagher
Creative Director Jo Cowan
Editorial Director Rosie McGuire
Senior Editor Carly Blake
Senior Designer Joe Jones
Consultant Janet Dyson
Production Elizabeth Collins, Jennifer Brunwin-Jones
Reprographics Stephan Davis, Jennifer Hunt
Assets Lorraine King

ISBN 978-1-78617-752-0

Printed in China

British Library Cataloguing-in-Publication Data
A catalogue record for this book is available from the British Library

ACKNOWLEDGEMENTS
The publishers would like to thank the following artists
who have contributed to this book:

Cover: Mëlanie Florian at The Bright Agency
Jan Lewis Page 20
All other artwork from the Miles Kelly Artwork Bank

The publishers would like to thank the following
sources for the use of their photographs:

Shutterstock.com 4(bird) jl661227, (ground) JinYoung Lee;
5(field) Emjay Smith; 6(background) Vinata; 10(grain) Sylverarts, (signpost) VikaSuh,
(cacti) Clipart deSIGN, (water bag) Yuran, (money bag) Clipart deSIGN; 12(sun) Andere,
(bags) Tribalium; 13(children) Andere, (children) White Sparrow; 15(money bags) Clipart
deSIGN; 17(coins) Enache Dumitru Bogdan; 20(money bags) Matthew Cole

Every effort has been made to acknowledge the source and copyright holder of each
picture. Miles Kelly Publishing apologises for any unintentional errors or omissions.

Made with paper from a sustainable forest

Contents

The Story of the Seeds

Jesus often taught people about God by telling them stories. Once, He told a story about a farmer who was sowing seeds in his field.

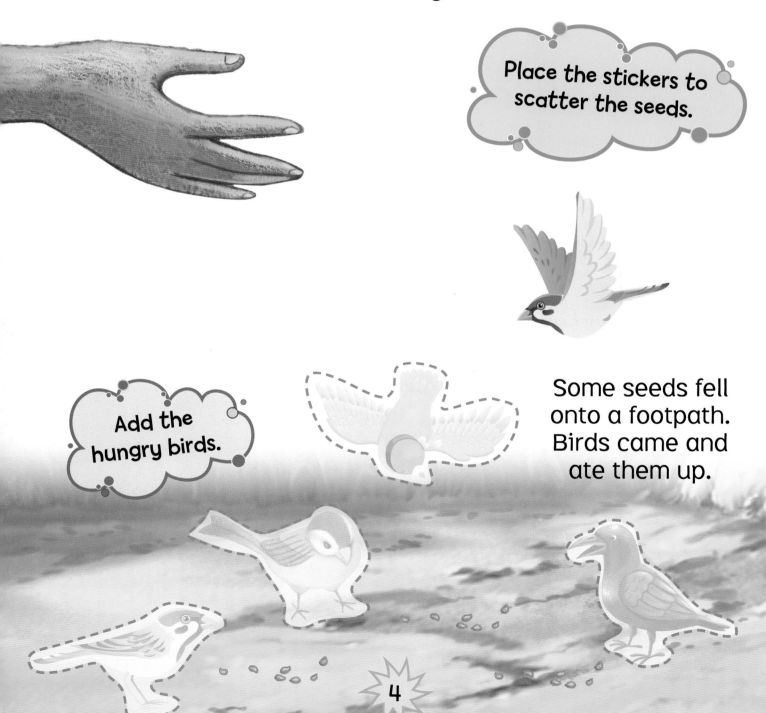

Place the stickers to scatter the seeds.

Add the hungry birds.

Some seeds fell onto a footpath. Birds came and ate them up.

Some seeds fell onto stony ground. Their roots could not grow, so they died.

Stony ground

Some seeds fell among weeds. The weeds grew quickly and choked them.

Weeds

Some seeds fell onto rich soil and they grew tall and strong. Jesus explained, "The seeds in the rich soil are like people who trust God. They will be good and happy."

Find the stickers of the plants in stony ground, weeds and rich soil.

Rich soil

The Good Samaritan

Jesus told a story about a Jewish man who was walking along the road from Jerusalem to Jericho. The man was attacked by robbers. They stole his belongings and ran away.

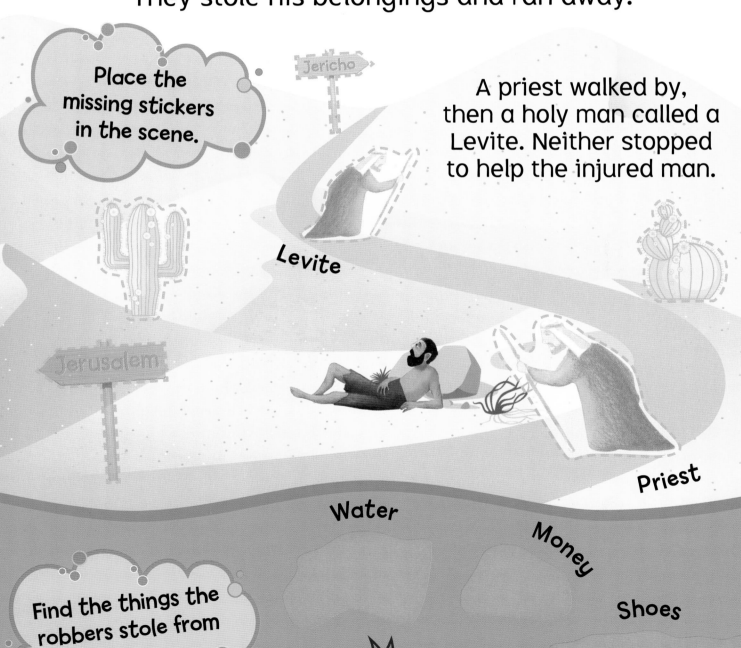

Place the missing stickers in the scene.

A priest walked by, then a holy man called a Levite. Neither stopped to help the injured man.

Jericho

Levite

Jerusalem

Priest

Water

Money

Shoes

Find the things the robbers stole from the man.

Jesus and the Children

One day, lots of children came to see Jesus. Jesus' friends told them to go away. But He said, "Let them come to me. To enter Heaven, everyone must be pure-hearted, like children."

Find the missing stickers and add butterflies in the sky.

Jesus

Children

Stickers for pages 4, 5 and 6

Jerusalem

Jericho

10

Stickers for pages 7, 8, 17 and 18

13

10

1

4

1

Two in the Temple

Jesus told a story about two men in a temple. One of them, a Pharisee, thought he was better than other people. He prayed loudly so everyone could hear him. The other man, a tax collector, was sorry for his sins. He hid away and prayed quietly.

Pharisee

Tax collector

Find the stickers to finish the picture.

God was more pleased with the humble tax collector than the proud Pharisee.

Count the tax collector's coins and stick the bags with the correct numbers on top.

The Good Shepherd

Jesus once said to a crowd, "If a shepherd saw a wolf attack his flock of sheep, what would he do? If he was a hired shepherd, working only for money, he would run away and save himself."

Put some birds in the sky.

Add more sheep to the flock and place the prowling wolf.

Wolf

Shepherd

Sheep

Jesus the good shepherd

"I am not like that," Jesus continued, "I am the good shepherd. I have many flocks in different places. I will look after all my sheep, no matter what."

Find the sticker of Jesus the good shepherd.

Jesus explained that the sheep in the story are people. He meant that He cares for all people, everywhere.

Place the stickers of the people.

A Story of Forgiveness

Jesus told a story about a farmer who had two sons. The younger son asked his father for some money, and went off to see the world.

Place the missing coins in the son's bags of money.

Find the stickers to finish the picture of the son and the pigs.

The son was foolish, and soon he had spent all his money. He had to find work, looking after pigs.

The son was unhappy so he went home to his father to say sorry. His father forgave him. He was so happy his son had returned, he threw a party and invited friends over.

Father and son

Find the stickers to finish the pictures.

Older son

The older son thought his father should be angry. But Jesus explained: "God is happy when sinners ask to be forgiven."

Place the stickers of the party guests.

The Lost Coins

Jesus told a story about a prince who had to travel away from his kingdom. The prince put three servants in charge while he was gone.

Place the correct number of gold bags for each servant.

First servant

The prince gave the first servant five bags of gold.

Second servant

He gave the second servant two bags of gold.

Third servant

And he gave the third servant one bag of gold.

While the prince was away, the first two servants used their gold to make more. When the prince returned he was pleased.

Find the stickers to finish the picture.

Prince

First servant

Third servant

Second servant

The third servant had hidden his gold and still had only one bag. The prince was angry. Jesus said that God is pleased with people who try hard.

Count how many bags each servant has and place the correct number on each circle.

Can You Remember?

Here are some questions about the stories in this book. Find the stickers that show the answers and place them on the coloured circles.

 What animals ate the seeds that fell onto the footpath?

Who helped the injured man on the road to Jerusalem?

 Who does Jesus describe as pure-hearted?

What did Jesus say the hired shepherd would do?

 What animals did the farmer's youngest son look after?

What did the prince leave his servants when he went away?

 How many bags of gold did the third servant have in the end?